Pure Posy

also by Posy Simmonds

MRS WEBER'S DIARY
TRUE LOVE
PICK OF POSY
VERY POSY
FRED

Pure Posy

POSY SIMMONDS

JONATHAN CAPE
THIRTY-TWO BEDFORD SQUARE LONDON

for Richard

First published 1987
Copyright © 1987 by Posy Simmonds
Jonathan Cape Ltd, 32 Bedford Square, London WC1B 3EL

British Library Cataloguing in Publication Data

Simmonds, Posy
Pure Posy.
I. Title
741.5'942   PR6069.I3

ISBN 0 224 02485 X

The drawings in this book have been taken from episodes of the weekly cartoon strip appearing in the *Guardian,* from *Harper's Magazine,* New York and from the *Sunday Times.*

Printed in Great Britain by
St. Edmundsbury Press, Bury St. Edmunds, Suffolk

© Posy Simmonds 1986

1986. The Year of the Tiger:

© Posy Simmonds 1986

Sandra.. if I said to you: someink **LOOKED** like a duck...n' **WALKED** like a duck...n' **QUACKED** like a duck...**what** would you call it?

DUCK, of course! Stands to reason...

Right... ..and if I'd said to you, **five** years ago... about this **middle-class** lot, here...'oo took this street over....

Cuckoo, Pippa!

...if I'd said: They **look** like **NOBS**......

****! My nail!

Careful with the claret, darling

...and they **LIVE** like **NOBS**....

Oh yeah! All **extensions** and **bidets**..& **utility rooms** ...& **au pairs** & **dinner parties**....

..and they **SOUND** like **NOBS**....

Oh, super, Gemma! See you both Saturday, sort of 8 for 8·30ish?

Super!

.... but they don't **THINK** like **NOBS**.....

At least if they invested in the infrastructure, **something** would be **done** about unemployment!

Quite!

And where's all the **North Sea** money going?!

Not into the Health Service, that's for sure!

NOT using the money from mortgage-interest tax relief... **NOT** putting that money directly into housing, is **CRIMINAL!**

If you can't rent & can't pay off a £25,000 mortgage where the hell **are** people expected to live !!?

I dunno HOW people can send their kids to **PRIVATE** schools!

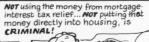

...you'd've called 'em?

Sort of middle-class **Socialists**....

Right!

Yeah..well.. my problem **is**... **what** d'you call this particular lot here, **nowadays**?........

...cos they still **LOOK** like ducks............but **now** they **QUACKS** like ducks!

Got a lot of **elbow**, this Brouilly, Leo!

...and they **LIVE** like ducks.....

Couldn't these go to the **cottage**, darling?

They're so **60's!**

cos I've seen the most perfect **C.19 silk moiré** at Rutland Antiques!

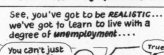

See, you've got to be **REALISTIC**... we've got to learn to live with a degree of **unemployment**....

You can't just **legislate** it away!

True

mm

I'm thinking of my poor **hernia**...**is** the London Clinic **VERY** pricey?

This house? Well..it should fetch **£190,000** if we're lucky...

..the local comprehensive's **SO DIRE!** I feel **FRIGHTFUL**, but really, we've **no option BUT** to send 'im privately......what does one **DO!**...

Oh I know!

And **how're** our **T.S.B. shares** doing today?

Tsk..Lor Love·a·duck...

© Posy Simmonds 1986

We bring you— live, from the scene of the tragedy.....

Alarms

 Anything wrong, Belinda? Nope... ..nuffing...

 Nothing's the matter, Mum... Stop hassling me...

Bust-up with that louche, Saab-driving Alistair?.... Yes ☐ No ☐

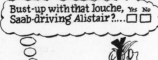

NOT Pregnant? Oh God!........ Yes ☐ No ☐

Herpes? Yes ☐ No ☐

Other unmentionable Diseases?......... Yes ☐ No ☐

Drink?... Yes ☐ No ☐

Drugs?... Yes ☐ No ☐

Debt?... Yes ☐ No ☐

Trouble with the Police? Yes ☐ No ☐

 Why did I do it?! Why!?

 Oh, I've been so stupid!

Weltschmerz? Yes ☐ No ☐

Terminal Sulking? Yes ☐ No ☐

Morning Mum!

Pregnant? Yes ☐ No ✓

© Posy Simmonds 1984

Who worries about the Worriers?

Mm..you do look a bit rough, Wendy...

I'm **FED UP!** I'm exhausted!

I mean, it's **TAKE, TAKE, TAKE...**all the time!

I spend the **whole** time coping with **THEIR** problems!

...**GEORGE,** for instance....well, I **know** it's worrying for him.....

..Now, listen, Wendy, will you...this is **MY** course the **Assessor's** damning.... He says "**A ragbag of intellectual faddishness.**" ...**PHILISTINE!** Even my "**La Pépinière de L'Apocalypse**", gets it in the neck!.... He calls for a "**caring system of structured modules**".....

I give up!

...and then there's my mother...

...didn't **EVEN** put my buns on the **stall**!... ..I had to say to her, "That's the last time I'm supporting **YOUR** Bring & Buy!"......

...And now she...she cut me in **Sainsbury's** ...and she won't come and play **Scrabble**! ∫ SNIFF ∫

Oh dear!

...and **Benji**.......and Tamsin....

Bud I wanded you to buy me **TRAINERS** for school.. Bweurr... **NOT** Gym shoes BooHoo

...And Mrs Taylor made me sit on the Trouble Seat all ...

C.F.

.....and Sophie.....

Course he'll ring you, Sophie... I'm sure he will...

HE WON'T!

SOB

...and why won't you led me have my ears pierced?

..and our babysitter:

Course he'll ring you, Trina...I'm sure he will...

He won't

...and the car...

Oh God, not more warning lights on all the time!

You've only just been serviced!

...and the cat....

PUSSY

There's a **limit!** I can't take any more!

I mean... **NO ONE EVER** says "Are you all right, Mum?"

...They **NEVER** ask!..... No one ever worries about **ME!** Never imagine that I might have my **OWN** worries...oh no!......

Have you got worries, Wendy?

Have **I** got **worries!?**

I'm worried about George... I'm worried about my mother... ...and Tamsin...and Sophie.... and the cat..and Trina...and...

© Posy Simmonds 1986

To a TREE...

In a certain street, residents are on the *qui vive*.....

Excuse ME!

Oh GAWD, not another!

Look...about this **TREE**.....

Listen, lady, *ORLRIGHT*...Don't say another word, *ORLRIGHT*?....
WE ARE NOT CUTTING IT DOWN!
...*ORLRIGHT*?

...nor no other tree in this street ...*ORLRIGHT*?

We *KNOW* this is a *CONSERVATION* area, *ORLRIGHT*?...*REPEAT*: we are not cutting it down...*we are LOPPING*...*ORLRIGHT*?

LOPPING?!

Now **LOOK!** Look up there! That's an 'Ealth 'Azard, that is!

You want *DODGY* branches falling on your *Volvo*? Eh?

We're only doin' our job, ..*ORLRIGHT*? We're only **lopping** it a little bit...

Why only a little?

Why can't you cut the *whole* thing down?!

WOT?!

I MEAN CUT IT DOWN! THIS WHOLE, BLOODY TREE! I've had it up to *HERE*!! *CUT it DOWN!* **DOWN!**

I mean, have *YOU* **LOOKED** what's round this tree? *HAVE YOU? HAVE YOU?* What's *THIS*!?

Wull...lot of *DOGS'* wossname....

Poo Poo

YES! DOGS' MESS!!! That's what I put up with **DAY IN...DAY OUT!** Outside my kitchen window!! All over the *KIDS'* shoes... ...push chair wheels!!

Why ME? Why THIS tree? The dogs *DO* it...but it's the *OWNERS'* fault...

I've done *EVERYTHING!* ..cleaned up with ammonia... ..remonstrated...*SHOUTED!*

...I've taken polaroids of the dogs and their owners and stuck them in the window as a **GALLERY** of **SHAME!**

...I draw chalk circles round the messes and date them...

...I've sprayed them with **GOLD** paint to make them look *prettier*...!

But it's *THIS TREE!!* It's a *MAGNET!* I'm asking you...*CUT* it *down!* **HACK** it *DOWN!*

Diabolical Woman!

I think I shall never see A poem lovely as a tree... Poems are made by fools like me.... But *DOGS* can make a lavatr'ee... *GROAN*

At the Poly, there is a rumour going round the staff canteen.......

LEAVING us, George?

"Fresh fields and pastures new..?"

WOODS!

Woods?

It's fresh **WOODS**...not **FIELDS**...

Anyway, this is strictly *entre-nous*.....O.K?

See, I think it's a..a great opportunity for me.....

Oooh, GEORGE! Moving out into the sunrise industries, are we!?

Oooh!

HmM.

Cor... Well, well.....we'll be sorry to lose you.....

No No No! Don't get me wrong!

I haven't decided yet..whether to...

Haven't decided YET!? Och, Good God, man! Hardly a difficult decision!

I mean, ye've been teaching here **quite** a wee while, noo...

17 years...

17...is that a fact? And what've ye got to show for your-r-r seventeen year-r-s?

Ye've got a wee space in the car park...

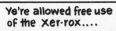

Ye're allowed free use of the Xer-rox....

Ye can make ootside calls **BEFORE** 1·00p.m...

You can claim your cassette tapes for dictating on EXPENSES

Ye've got a wee armchair in your office...

...and carpet tiles...

You can bring in a **fan heater** during cold weather...

You're allowed **TICK** here, in the canteen... and your own little **MUG**...

That's what you've got in **17 YEARS.**

Yeah...I know...

So **HOW** can you **THINK** of giving all that up!!?

Don't do it, man!

GEORGE

© Posy Simmonds 1986

Union Jakes

In the Brass Monk, the *Webers* are discussing *Britain's* decline with some Americans:

No, that's wrong!

...I mean, you're **right**, **CLASS DISTINCTIONS** here are **still** more than **vestigial**....but they simply **aren't** as **rigid** as you've been implying....

Hey, but you still haven't explained why you're so **infantile**.. I mean, your **dirdy yumor**...**WHY** are the Briddish **so** obsessed with that kinda **anal** stuff?

I mean... you're **RE**tards!

Don't think we're **MORE** obsessed than anyone else......in **Europe**...I mean, there's a long tradition of...of **robust** humour...**Chaucer**...**Rabelais**... ....but I wouldn't call us **OBSESSED**

Evening, Cod's eyes!

Well, I guess you guys must know.........way **I** see it, this country is still kinda upta-here in **class divisions**

...like I said before, it's your **main** preoccupation...

...**THAT**...and **toilet** yumor

Class and **what**?

Toilet yumor ...you guys find toilets **funny**

Do **you**, Wendy?

Toilets?!

I don't **talk** about **class**...or **toilets**... ...much...

I **NEVER** talk about **toilets**! **HORRIBLE** word!

Oh really Wendy!

IS it?

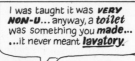 

I was taught it was **VERY NON-U**... anyway, a **toilet** was something you **made**... ...it never meant **lavatory**.

Ooh, you say **LAVATORY**, do you?

...There's **POSH**!

Well, I say **LOO** sometimes.....

Oh, I hate **LOO**!

Yuppies say **LOO**...

...you see **loo's** more a middle class euphemism... and **lavatory's** more upper-class... ...and **toilet's**...

At my prep school! we used to call it the **REARS**

Rears, eh?

We called it the **BOG**....

We called it the **AUNT**

..Or the **Slasher**... ...Or the **JAKES**..

I don't call it anything... I just go off to shake a tail feather ...or to pop a **cork**! Her Her Her Heh Heh

...or to go and **change** the barrel!

Her Her Haaa!

..pump the bilges...go and kill a hedge!

HAAAA! AHAHA HAHAA! HAAA HAAA!

Omigard! Retards!

Go where the big knobs hang out! —HAAAAA HAA HAA!

© Posy Simmonds 1986

Giving Up

Edmund Heep is propping up the bar of the *Castle & Ball*...

That's another 2 pints of 3 star, please, Joy..

Like your *sixth* pint in a glass, Maurice?

Or d'you want it as an *intravenous drip* —and cut out the middleman!!?

AHAR HAR HA! Har Har!!

Her her her!

Here, Edmund..... got a *FAG* on you? I'm gasping...

Gasping, are you? Oh dear!

Hey! You *HAVEN'T* given it up, have you?

No..but I've got the old *faggeroons* well under control!

What! *YOU*?!

Yes! I tell you! It's called *self discipline!*

It's a *HABIT*, smoking, isn't it? How many d'*you* smoke without thinking?

..Dunno

Well, there you are!

I, ...I have so *disciplined* myself......

..that, now, I *NEVER* smoke mindlessly.... but always for a reason...

I count every fag & make every fag count!

Result is... *DRAMATIC* reduction!!

What you do is, wrap the pack up, like this, in paper and rubber bands...so it's hard to get at.....

What's the pencil 'n' paper for?

..to *LOG* the time of the cigarette... and to answer the question you must always ask yourself: *"Why do I want this fag? Why do I smoke?"*

What, so you write: "because I feel *TENSE*".. or "made a right Horlicks of the *sales* returns"..... or...

You got it!

Let's have a look then...

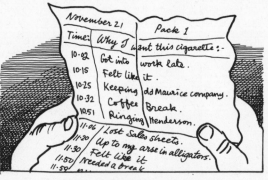

November 21   Pack 1

Time:	Why I want this cigarette :-
10·02	Got into work late.
10·15	Felt like it.
10·25	Keeping old Maurice company.
10·32	Coffee Break.
10·51	Ringing Henderson.
11·06	Lost sales sheets.
11·20	Up to my arse in alligators.
11·30	Felt like it
11·50	Needed a break
11·59	

God! Two packs! And 19 just between tea-time and... *NOW!*

Not bad going, eh?

Have one on me.. I'm just off to shake a tail feather

© Posy Simmonds

© Posy Simmonds 1986

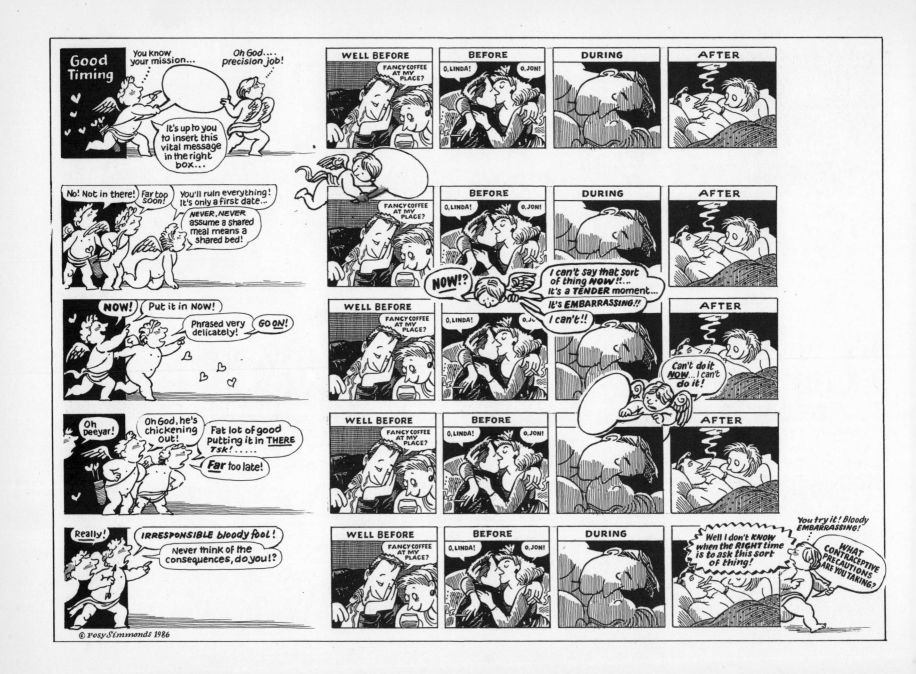

© Posy Simmonds 1986

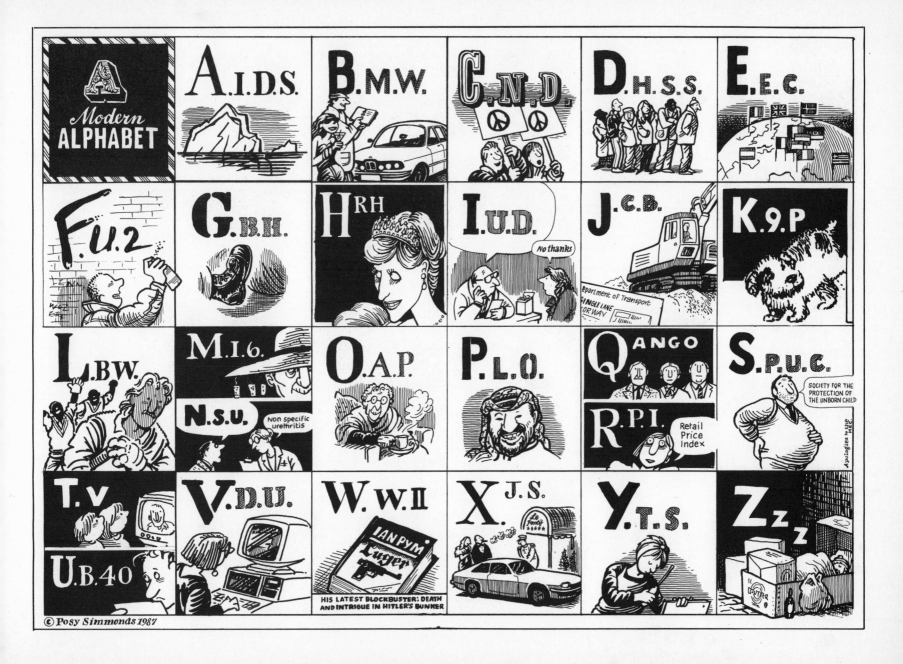

What Money can buy

No, Bev! Really?

How it feels a cellular phone costs? than the £1000!

What's this, Wendy!? Bev tells me she's being *PRIVATELY* educated!

Really?

She certainly *isn't!*...Well... not....

I AM Mum!

Oh, Wendy, Wendy! Come on!

It's ALL RIGHT, Wendy........ now, now!

But it's not like...

Oh, Wendy, I know JUST how you feel...We felt *exactly* the same when we took Tara away from her comprehensive.....

It was absolute AGGERS!

Don't feel BAD, ..honestly...

It's *not HERESY* any more...We've ALL done it...

EVERYONE round here's......

I mean...you HAVE to think of the children.... Why should we make them suffer for *our* principles?

It's *not fair*....Tara HATED *Fletcher Montacute*...absolutely LOST in those *huge* classes!

And those boys! She never learnt ANY Maths at all...the girls could *never* get NEAR the computer terminals.....

And she's doing *so* well at *Plumcote Hall* - ADORES it there! Doing ten 'O' Levels... fencing...

Costs an arm and a leg each term, but...well...

I mean, I *know*, an *fond*, it's wrong...but...

It *is* wrong!

It's GOT to be wrong to BUY privilege!

How ARE the state schools going to get any better, if the *middle classes* have no interest in putting pressure on the system?

We all ought to contribute to the social mix...

For all its faults, Bev's staying put at Thomas Craweley...I feel very strongly about it.

Oh, but I THOUGHT Bev said she was...

Oh, THAT?

Well, yes, she was er... falling behind a bit ...and...yes... she does have a bit of help at home...

Aha! Little *PRIVATE COACHING*, eh?

Not like that at all!... ...it's just, well...Crispin Naylor pops in and..er... helps her with her Maths and Science in the evenings....that's all...

For M·O·N·E·Y?

Well, yes... we DO pay him.... I mean, I feel sorry for these graduates...he hasn't found a proper job yet...

I see-ee

Told you I had a PRIVATE TUTOR!

Pot-head Revisited

When *Crispin Naylor*, (lately down from *varsity*), comes to coach *Beverley* in O Level Maths and French......

Ah, Crispin!

O, hallo, sir...

....the *Webers' house* is filled with the scent of *Harris Tweed* and *Bay Rum* and pipe tobacco and *very* old brogues......

Sir indeed!

He's like something out of "*Brideshead Revisited*"!

...And after tuition, there's tea and toast and conversation......

Of course, I *despise* those days... I utterly deplore the values of that generation....

...and the *SHAMBLES* they made of their lives and the world......

It was *SUCH* an utterly *FILTHY* epoch...*immoral*...*degenerate*... ...their *tacky idealism*...their ghastly *enlightenment* and *liberalism*.....

...that was the beginning of *YOB-RULE*, God-help-us!

Filthy, *FILTHY* decade!

When?

I see

YOUR lot, Dad...the *SIXTIES*..we were just saying how *revolting & immoral & dissolute* and *degenerate* they were...

Yeah, even Dad...he went overland to Turkey in a sweaty bus with a lot of girls...didn't you, Dad? ...*AND* you had *LOVE-INS* at university......

There is *ONE* aspect of that era, whose passing I mourn...where one's revulsion melds with...a *genuine NOSTALGIA* for a vanished way of life....

SIGH

..a way of life *WE* shall *never* know... ≥SIGH≤ none of *us*... ......

When I imagine all those depraved creatures, playing in the sunlight....

...before the shadows lengthened and the world was plunged into gloom...they seem like *long, lost golden afternoons*, the Sixties....

SIGH

Wot?

...the Sixties...when one could go to bed with everyone, without fear of getting *AIDS*...and *Herpes*..,...

...and cervical cancer...

Hmm... *All you need is Love* ??

© *Posy Simmonds* 1986

W.O.T.

A Doctor Warns

Q: What is W.O.T.?

W.O.T. stands for Wilfully Over-Tasked. ......it is a *serious* social problem....

Here is a typical W.O.T. case:

And where're you sloping off to, George? Eh?

Erm...I'm just nipping upstairs...to..er..finish putting my **lecture slides** in order......

God! You and your *bloody* work!

Can't you **LEAVE** it for **once**!!?

It's **BANK HOLIDAY**!

Just cos you don't want to help the kids with their Easter Egg hunt!

You don't understand, Wendy... I **MUST** finish this lecture, by...

Tsk God!

W.O.T. The Informalist Backlash

BUT YOU NEVER STOP working!! I'm **SICK** of it!!! You're a bloody **WORKAHOLIC!**

This man, George W., needs help. He is Wilfully Over-Tasked...he is *chronically* addicted to **WORK**, and this is causing grave damage to his domestic life......

Now, **MODERATE WORKING** does no one any harm...our systems can cope with it...it makes us feel *important*, *bushy-tailed*, and so on....

But, what starts out as *taking-a-bit-of-work-home*, can so easily turn to a **DEPENDENCE**, which excludes everything else.

Once addicted, recovery is often unpleasant, involving severe withdrawal symptoms. This man had a 92 hour-a-week work habit.....

My wife left me...

Are **YOU** Wilfully Over-Tasked? If you answer **YES** to more than one of the following questions.... ...then maybe it's time you took a serious look at your work habit......

Do you plead pressure of work to avoid irksome situations?

Look, I can't make the Parents' Evening at the school...

I've got to redraft this report...

Do you bore others with your preoccupation with work?

..I couldn't get back here, before now...I was up to my arse in alligators and then Pope comes in and asks for the February figures..and...

Do you cause unecessary stress to the unwaged?

GRR! I've got **SO** much **WORK**!

You should be so lucky...

Housework isn't **REAL** work. Do you agree?

Do you think about work in bed?

£120,000 £150,000? 3½%

WOT! Still WORKING?

?

Rough Winds do blow.....

The Webers have taken advantage of the Bank Holiday to make an excursion into the countryside, with family and friends......

Having reviewed the Spring.....

How much further?

It's raining again!

...they repair to a hostelry....

I'll just give these to George

OK, Tom

Yes, *wasn't* that **lovely**..seeing the buds...

...I mean, in town, the kids're completely *CUT OFF*.. I mean, they just can't sort of get to **experience**...the *THRILL* of each season, can they?

..and it's so good for them to see a bit of.. folklore.... tradition....

God...I'm worried about George...

Oh yes!

..well, bought him a pie and a pint... ..& merely remarked "This is the life!" ...and he *BIT my HEAD* off!

?

!

Yes! He went on & on !

What's so bloody wonderful about it?

...Just another day *WASTED!*

Bloody **HOLIDAYS!**

I've *got* to behave as though I'm *RELAXED*.. & I *can't* relax, 'cause I'm too busy thinking it's **MONDAY**... Just makes a great *DENT* in my lecture programme... I'll more or less have to give the last one *AGAIN*, so the students can pick up the thread... *Tsk!* ...Oh God!

.. And all this bloody phony *folksy* atmosphere!! Mini-buses full of *Morris* men... silly 'folklore' uniforms...bar full of *John Balls*...agri-businessmen...talking antiques!.....

I could be wading through that pile of *theses* assessments

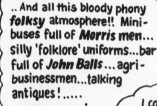

You go off, Tom... don't mind me... You go and enjoy yourself...

Oh don't take any notice...

...he always behaves like that, when it's his turn to sit with the kids.....

The House-Keeping

© Posy Simmonds 1985

Pilgrimage

Whan that Aprille with his shoures sote, The droght of March hath perced to the rote. Than longen folk to goon on Diets, at places of Purgation:

Many are they who embark, who have sat by flesh pots & eaten bread and have waxed fat....

And others, stiff-necked people, full of affliction, & those that are vain, yet full of care....

Each shall put on loose raiment...

...and go before those in judgement over them. For their sins are numbered,

...and many and various are the ways of chastisement.

And thenceforward, five nights & days shall they repent, eschewing all meat and wine,

...mortifying the flesh and meditating on the folly of their ways.

And some do undergo a fiery torment.....

...and do cast out devils...

...and others do force their joints to go off like pistols and their hamstrings to cry out...

And others do confess diverse heresies and are shriven.

And when the days of their tribulation are accomplished, they are absolved.

Most have endured great losses. But some are still like great Bulls of Bashan; And some have masticated secretly, and are found out.

And then all do depart, & break their fast, & go on their way rejoicing.....

Posy Simmonds ©

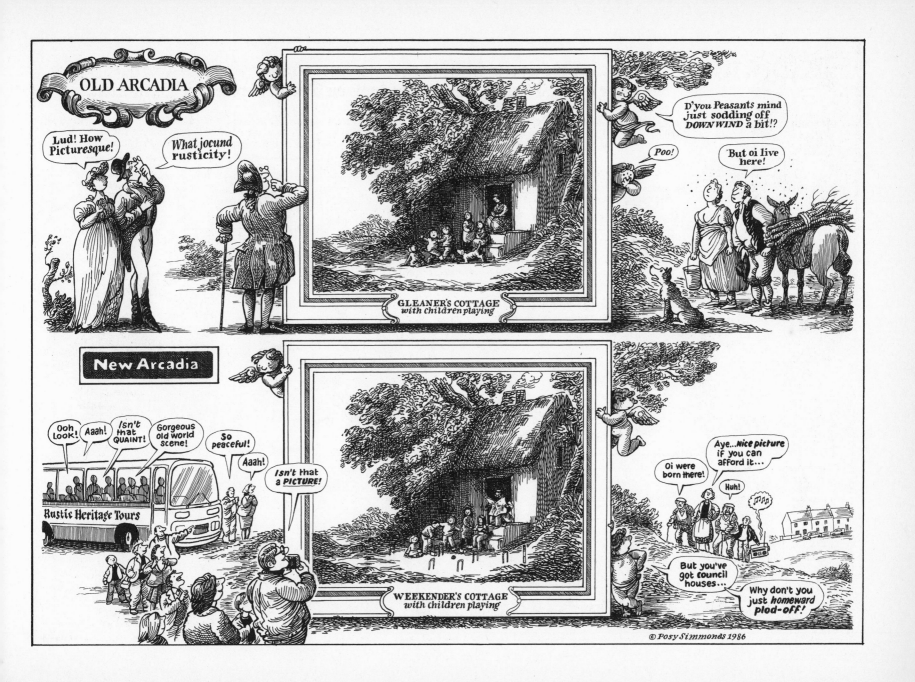

© Posy Simmonds 1986

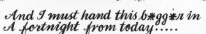

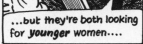

A Mother's Plea

Dear Agony Aunt.....I am the mother of three small children....I look quite young, but feel a hundred.....

I live high above the city. The place is cold, filthy and verminous and the air polluted. I fear for my children's health.

I was led to believe that the rôle of **Mother** was **sacred** and **hallowed**, that its duties were of the most **vital importance** to Society....and that people would look up to me in reverence...

KKOO COO

But they do not. Beneath me the World goes about its **real** concerns, as if I do not exist....

I'm ignored.... taken for granted, at best, an obstacle to be negotiated on the pavement...

I spend my long domestic days in isolation.....mute, passive, without identity.....

COO!

People only take notice of me when I become **unstable**.....it's not my fault—the traffic shakes my foundations.....

My God! She's unsteady!

If that Mother falls, someone could get hurt!

Then, **the Authorities** call me a **Danger to Society**....and rail against mothers as the source of every social evil...

DAILY THING
THE FACE OF EVIL:
ACCUSED KILLER BLAMES OVER-PROTECTIVE MOTHER

Daily Other
LATCH-KEY KIDS ARE TOMORROW'S MUGGERS says Judge

They are threatening to take away my **Child Benefit** and replace it with a means-tested credit.....I feel I'm **cracking up** completely.......Please help....**Mother of Three**.

An Inspiration to Us All!

It is tea time in the *Weber* household....

♪ Pom...Pom...Pom ♪

Now, Benji...beans **ON** toast..or **OFF**?

I want mine **ON**!

OFF!

♪...Pom ♪ Pom ♪ Pom... Pom...

♪ Pom...Pom...Pom...

"MY KIDS BEFORE MY *CAREER!*" says best-selling romantic novelist Lorna Jay, in a frank interview with...

HEINZ

" Really, I'm a wife and mother first and then a writer", smiled Janet Lee, alias Lorna Jay, whose glowing red-haired looks belie her 35 years. Just a wife & mother? That statement will come as a shock to the millions of readers, world-wide, who lap up every word she pens.

We were talking in the pink and gold, second floor drawing room of her London home...a lovely, lived-in room, full of the Art Deco bric-a-brac which she & her company director husband, Ron Grossman, have collected on their many trips abroad. Besides the London home, there is an 18th century, Wiltshire mansion and a luxuriously converted barge, moored at Bray-on-Thames.

Just then, the door burst open: Carlton (5) and Robyna (6) were home from school, plus the other member of the family, a golden retriever called 'Honey'. All were greeted fondly before being whisked off to tea by Nanny.

"They're my life!" Lorna said, after they'd gone, her eyes shining. "I'm very close to them.... above all, we're such tremendous friends!"

"I'm so really PRIVILEGED in my life", she went on, "When I think of other people's lives...I've got so MUCH!.... houses, travel, celebrity parties.... but, believe me, my biggest goal is creating a happy home ..."

"And it takes effort! Even when I'm in faraway places, I HAVE to call my kids at their bedtime... Family togetherness is such a precious thing...it's a GIFT you owe your children...after all, they're only with us such a short time..."

"I've never understood the conspiracy to make mothers...housewives feel inferior...cabbages... THEY'RE the unsung heroines! Rearing the FUTURE just has to be the most important, difficult job! MOTHER...HOUSEWIFE are badges I wear with pride!" she glowed...

", and it really makes me sad when I hear of home-makers portrayed as bored, oppressed, alcoholic and ..."

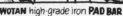

Household tips from Household Gods...

AT THIS TIME OF YEAR, YOU MORTALS TRY TO APPEASE US HOUSEHOLD GODS, BY PURIFYING YOUR HEARTHS OF ALL MANNER OF VILENESS. THIS RITUAL YOU CALL SPRING CLEANING....

HERE ARE SOME TIPS ON THE REMOVAL OF THE MORE STUBBORN HOUSEHOLD FILTH.....

GROUND-IN DIRT:

Tsk!

ONCE-OVER **ZAP!** ENDS FILTHY-FLOOR NIGHTMARE IN SECONDS!

ZAP

DRIED-ON DIRT:

SPRAY WITH *Bio-Flak*... ...THEN WIPE.....

Bio Flak

YELLOW WAXY BUILD-UP:

Euch! Omigod!

Causto-flor CLEANS RIGHT THRU TO THE SHINE!

CRUSTED CORNERS:

Eeeuch!

SPRAY WITH *PURT* LEAVE A MOMENT... WIPE CLEAN...

HEAVY SOILING

OhGawd!

SOAK OVERNIGHT IN *BIO-BLAT*...THEN RINSE THRU....

BIO BLAT

TELL-TALE TOILET TIDE-MARK:

Ooh dear!

TOILET UNSIGHTLYNESS!? JUST **KILL** it!

KILL

RADIOACTIVE DUST:

WhAAat?

RADIOACTIVE DUST....THIS IS VERY STUBBORN AND DOES NOT RESPOND TO MORTAL INGENUITY........

WE SUGGEST THE TIME-HONOURED METHOD:— CHECK FOR OMENS IN THE ENTRAILS OF BEASTS, THE MILK OF CATTLE, THE EGGS OF BIRDS...

ISOLATE THOSE AFFLICTED...MARK THEIR DOOR WITH A SIGN:

WEAR CHARMS... MAKE SACRIFICES... MAKE SCAPEGOATS... ...AND ABOVE ALL, <u>PRAY</u>.....

CAUTION: TRY NOT TO MAKE RADIOACTIVE DUST. IT ALWAYS LANDS UP IN THE LAP OF THE GODS.

1. Heresies and Blasphemies:

"Come on, Sophie... it's important... You haven't come with us for AGES!"

"DID! I went at Easter!"

"Easter's MONTHS ago... and then we had to drag you along! ...You OUGHT to want to come! ....Your friends'll be there.... you like singing...."

"Uh GOD!"

"I HATE the singing! I HATE the standing! I HATE the sitting!"

"And all that sort of PAL-SEY-WALSEY, holy atmosphere just cracks me right up!"

"I don't BELIEVE in it! It...doesn't DO anything... just a total time-waste!"

"I'm NOT coming!"

2. Supplication:

"I see... Sophie, don't you CARE about things, anymore?"

"Don't you care about your life? OUR life? Everyone's life? Don't you CARE?"

"Yeah, yeah"

"Well, SHOW you care! Come with us now...it's only round the corner..."

"I'll think about it here..."

"Sophie...NONE of us can just THINK any-more! We've ALL got to DO!"

"Yeah, well you do, then."

"I'm ashamed of you...."

"...and you ought to be ashamed of yourself..."

"Come on, children, we must go...."

3. Heavenly Intervention:

"YATTA!!!! YATTA!!!"

"Wossat?"

"Hey! Police helicopter!"

"Hey! Whole place is crawling with Old Bill!"

"Hey! There's a TV crew!"

"Yeah!"

"It'll be on TELLY! Won't be a ruck, will there?"

"Coming?"

"Sophie! You've come! I'm so glad!"

NUCLEAR DUMPING NO!

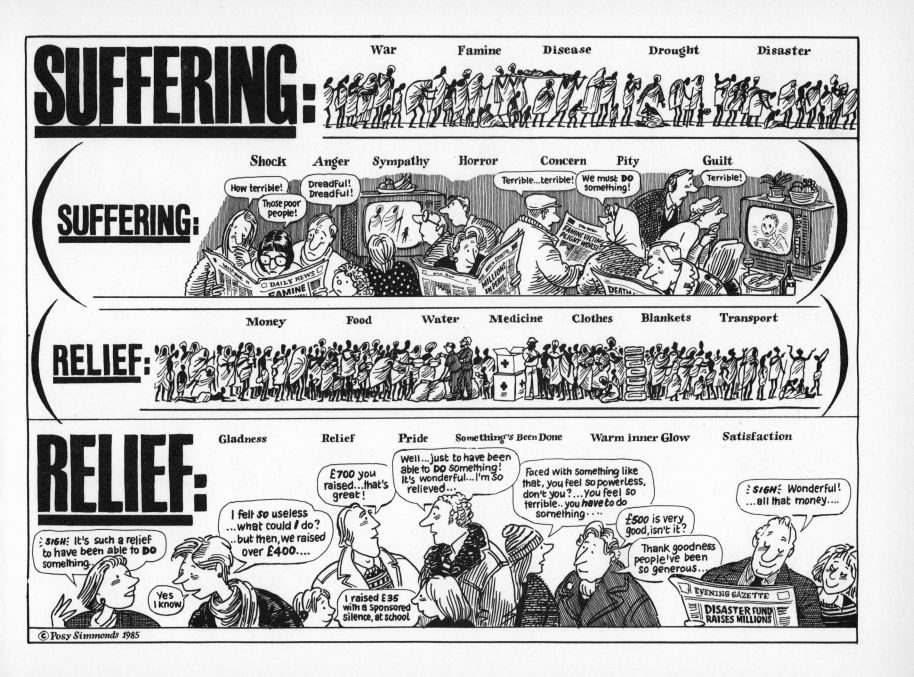

JUST past it

"Well, I *think* the message *is* getting through....."

"...one hears the most *unlikely* people talking about *condoms* now, doesn't one?"

"Yes, *everywhere!*"

"P'raps I'll try the *goat cheese*"

"Is it very *goaty?*"

"But they're still forecasting *200,000 infected* with the *virus* by *1988*, aren't they?"

"And that's *tip of the iceberg...* ...*tip of the iceberg.....*"

"...so I've *read* somewhere...."

"*Poor* young people... I feel so sorry for them... ...*IMAGINE* their *sex* lives......"

"Yep! Puts the kibosh on the old *wild oats*"

"Glad my salad days are long gone....."

"*NOT* talking about *wild oats...*"

"..I'm saying..in future, even two *unspotted virgins*'ll have the screens rushed round and a *blood test* or two zapped on them, before they *hold hands...*"

"Mm...*imagine* what their parties'll be like... *PARANOIA!*"

"No more *smooching* in corners...."

"Oh yes... *kissing's* in the *doghouse*, now, isn't it..."

"*Is it?*"

"Well, not sort of *hello/goodbye* kissing...that's O.K....."

"There *is* a theory that the *AIDS virus* has been around a lot longer than the last few years...or so I read somewhere......."

"Ah"

"*EH?!*"

"*Whaat?*"

"Eh?"

"*How* long?"

"Well...there's a lot they *don't* know about *lymph nodes* & their pathology.... ...you know, the *electron microscope* hasn't been around for ever....."

"But, *AIDS*...how long's *that* been around?"

"*Before 1969*, say..?"

"Well, *could* be....but they just *don't KNOW...* ...I mean, it's only *conjecture....*"

"Oh God"

"Oh *really*, Belinda..... don't let's start being *DEPRESSING!*"

Nature abhors a Vacuum

So...both your kids'll be at school **ALL** day in September?

Yes! Isn't it wonderful when they reach a *civilised* age?!

Can you bring the cakes, Wendy?

I mean, I *know* they're lovely when they're *littler*......

...but it's such *hard work*.... all those broken nights... **NAPPIES**...

...all those **ZOO**-like smells..... sweaters covered in dribble....

Mm...these look good

...and *never* having a minute alone... except if you lock yourself in the bog...

...and not being able to leave them with people...and feeling *guilty* if you do...

And people treating you like a *half-wit* & being all *condescending* when you say you don't work **OUTSIDE** the home.....

...and, really, you just feel so *flaked out* the whole time...

LICK!

Ah...it's a real relief to have got them to this stage...really *civilised* ...I can't believe it...

..I shall have these long uninterrupted mornings... afternoons too...& I only have to do the *school run* one week a month..

So what will you do? Go back to teaching...do a PhD...do the hospital *Mobile library?*

...thing is...I thought I'd have another baby...

© Posy Simmonds

Cheerful Thoughts

They **WHAT!?** **HIT** an old lady!!?

Yes! Two seven year olds...at the twins' school....

God! All this **VIOLENCE!** What a world to bring a child into!

Don't worry, Jane...I'm sure yours is going to be a model baby...

How can you be so sure?

Kids from nice homes are just as likely to turn out **EH?**

NICE homes!? Meaning **what**, exactly?

Winnie-the-Pooh-reading **MIDDLE-CLASS** homes?...with gardens...and *Postman Pat* wall charts?...whole place **stuffed** to busting with consumer durables...?

That what you mean?

Oh **shuddup**, George.....I mean **ANY** sort of home where the **parents CARE**...where the kids are taught to consider other people...where they learn **certain values**...

Ah, yes..where they learn **CERTAIN VALUES**....which are then shot to smithereens, soon as they switch on **TV**..or step outside the front door!

Oh.. Cheerful!

Fat chance **CERTAIN VALUES** have in our **HORRIBLE, VIOLENT AGGRESSIVELY MATERIALISTIC** society!

Well, of course **NURTURE** has a lot to do with how kids turn out......

...and **NATURE**...

...and **CHANCE**....

But I'm sure a lot of **NURTURE** helps...you'll be **terrific** in that department....

Gee, thanks..

Oh, **JANE'S** here! How nice! How **ARE** you?

Had a good snooze, Mummy?

You look **blooming!**... ..and **how's** the **BUMP?** Doesn't time fly!

Oh, he's fine!

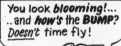

Oh, it's a **HE**, is it?

Yes, they could tell from my amniocentesis test....

...He **KICKS** like anything!

Aaah! That's lovely! Good **strong kicks!**...P'raps he's going to be **Nureyev!** ..or a **FOOTBALLER**...! ...or a little **Football hooligan!!!**

HA HA! Ah Dear!

Oh..

Have I said something wrong?

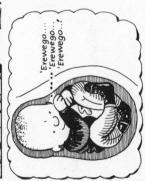

'Erewego... 'Erewego... 'Erewego...'

babaware

70-80 cm

0-6 month

cash

Excuse me....**THIS**... I'm not sure if he needs the 80 or the **90** centimetres...

For him, is it ?..Your little grandson?

I BEG your pardon?

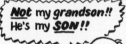

Not my **grandson!!** He's my **SON!!**

Oh **sorry!**

Really!

Didn't **mean**...

Well, I **know** it's second time round...um...my **second** wife.... but I'm not **all THAT**...um.... I mean, **YES**, I do have an **older** family...but I'm certainly not a **grandfather** . . . .

NO NO NO!

um...well, I think you'll find the 80 cm is right for him...

Thank you

check out

exit

© Posy Simmonds 1985

babaware

© Posy Simmonds 1987

NINE till FIVE

SUNDAY...

Here...want the *Review* bit?

Oh God...I *SHOULDN'T*, really... *SIGH!* Got that piece to write on *County Life-Style*, for Thursday...

Poor you!

MONDAY...

SOAKS WINE BAR

No, No, I mustn't...well... just a *QUICK* one...see', I've got this bloody article.... **6,000** words to do by **Thursday**

Poor you!

Want the 9 o'clock news?

No, listen, I'm not really watching... I've got that article to write.....

Oh poor you!

TUESDAY...

He says, can you come back at 4..? it'll be ready then

No, sorry...it'll have to wait... I'm *frantic* this afternoon...

RY CLEANERS

Milk

FERGIE'S FASHION FEVER!

WEDNESDAY...

No, really.. *I can't*...I've got this thing to write by tomorrow... ...We·ell, p'raps a *TINY* drink.... ...by the way, did you get **6 DOWN**, "flowing letter to a girl"..*five letters?*

Oh God! Is that the time!? I MUST fly!...Got this *sodding* piece to write..!

O poor you!

Look, tell her I'll ring her back...I can't speak now...I've got this bloody piece to do...

TACKA TACKA

Yes, I KNOW what time it is!

THURSDAY

Ah, here it is!....*SUPER!*

Poor you ..you look rough...

God, I mean! *What a WEEK!!!* ...and **9** last night till **5** this morning!...I mean...they just don't understand what it's like!

Dunno *how* you stand it

© Posy Simmonds 1986

Flying Fur

In the Toy Department, besides *dolls* and *little plastic men*, covered in weaponry, there are lots & lots of *furry animals*....

...There are *teddies* and *pandas* and *woof-woofs* and *pussy cats*..

...*bunny-wunnies* and *chick-chicks* and *quack-quacks* and *goosey-ganders*....and *foxies* and *jumbos* and *oink-oinks*...

...*All* of whom, as representatives of the *Animal Kingdom*, are absolutely *FED UP* to the back teeth with the *Human Race*.

© Posy Simmonds 1985

© Posy Simmonds 1984

Turning an Honest Penny

Times have been tough in Tresoddit... ...for *Kevin Penwallet*, ex-lecturer in anthropology....

...Lean season has followed lean season... and, in the end, even the ideals of strong men, bow to the prevailing economic draught....

"See, Kevin...you got to consider *what* the visitors *really* WANT!"

...and now, *Kevin Penwallet*, ex-purveyor of all that is *NATURAL*, has given over his shelves to *NATURE*....

For NATURE is *everywhere*! All over the tea-towels & cosies & oven gloves & scatter cushions & mob-capped jars of preserves....

...All over the sets of plates...& little hand-bells & figurines, and even the *slate pictures*, which Kevin, against his better nature, creates himself...

And Kevin's *better nature* does revolt!

"O God! O God!"

"ME! ME of all people....!! Perpetuating the MYTH!! This MYTH! which excludes TRUTH... excludes any REALITY... of the HARSHNESS of Nature and Country Life!"

"Oh God OhGod!"

Announcing a most important porcelain plate collection.....

THE PENWALLET PLATES

No.6 Dog Caught Short on Beach

But *how* can one deplore this peddling of Nature...with its whimsy...its sentiment, its bogus gentility...its nostalgia...when the till rings all day...and two village girls have been given employment?

As he sits at the back of the shop, scratching a masted schooner upon slate, Kevin dreams of a way of righting the balance, regarding Nature & the Country...of telling it like it is...

"That's £21.50 thank you...."

"Oh..and this ..cosy..."

The Fo'c's

The Haunting Beauty of our Coastline Heritage, recaptured in finest porcelain, by one of Europe's master craftsmen!

In his first series of collector's plates, the severely-gifted artist, *Kevin Penwallet*, has set out to recreate all the intriguing magnificence of our *Sea-Girt Isles*...hand-painted, in vivid, ceramic colours, upon exquisite, white porcelain.

The Collection portrays 12 dramatically different aspects of our spume-soaked shores... each plate a full 5¼" in diameter ...to preserve all the remarkable detail, that is a hallmark of Penwallet's art.

Marvel at "Oil-Drenched Gannet"...every oily feather faultlessly exact, as it expires amongst the plastic flotsam of the shoreline!
Marvel again at "Lonely Windsurfer"...the expression on the lad's face, as, gusted by a mischievous off-shore wind, he drifts far, far out to sea, beyond the reach of the Inshore Rescue Service!
Note the shimmering beauty of "Hauling in the Catch": A brace of boats lie at anchor, upon a limpid sea... In the foreground, burly Customs Officers haul in their day's catch of heroin, while the saucy smugglers dream of the years of enforced idleness that lie ahead!

Masterly beyond words, is Penwallet's "Leisure Centre at Eventide"......the lofty buildings straddling both sides of the once bosky peninsula. ....whilst "Dog caught short on Sandcastle," places the artist in the ranks of the World's most Outstanding

Animal Portraitists......and who could resist the sheer sentiment of "Old Village Post Office," with its queue of redundant china-clay workers ...characters, all!

The Penwallet Plates will inevitably attract admiration from all those who see them on your wall... but this limited edition is available only to those collectors who enter their subscriptions before October 1st 1985... £25 per plate.

Oil-Drenched Gannet

The Penwallet Plates
Tresoddit CORNWALL
Yes! RUSH me my Penwallet collection of 12 distinctive, Porcelain plates
I enclose cheque for £ _____
Name _____
Address _____

© Posy Simmonds 1985

French Impressionists

The Webers and friends from France pause after visiting the *Royal Academy*...
(BRITISH ART in the Twentieth Century)

...et les couleurs! Superbes! Extra!

Ravissantes!

COLOUR?...Well, *I* thought we British weren't, *perhaps*, the greatest colourists...

AH, non, Georges!

That's big injustice!

You are GENIUS!.... the colour I see, eezer SUBLIME!

Really?

Oh, well... thank you!

See... I'd always thought our LIGHT, here, was the trouble... ...you know, it's dull and grey... ...it affects our visual..um...

Well. Of course. In every case, zer visuelle mentalité of a culture is always a question of errr... ...wezzaire and géographie...

Yes. I tell you: *I* 'ave the *impression* of your leetle island, weeth eets *atrocité* of wezzaire...eets *profondeur* of greyness....

...weeth eets artistique psychologie, always languishing, to no great effect,...

...to EMBRACE...

..the BRILLIANCE and PASSION of the warm south...

...Provence... Le Midi...

SIGH: Yes...not much inspiration, here...wet fields & sodden nettles...

But you are WRONG! You ignore your World GENIUS!!!

We do?

Yes! You underrate yourselves!...Out of your wet, Breeteesh paysage of small, domestic narrative...this douceur of leetle hill & wood, wheech lacks everything dramatic and sauvage...OUT of thees WETNESS, you are inspired to create... ...des MERVEILLES!!

Marvels?

Mais, si! Master-pieces of colour and texture.... wheech express everything of your rain & wind & steam!...Think of all your great names!

Turner?

O.. Non, TURNER!

Non! I mean 'ARRIS TWEED... ...Burberry...Barbour..!

et Pringle!

O...ce cardigan en cachemire! O...superbe! Extra!

O chouette!

O, les kilts!

McTav

Row 1

The driver of an expensive car....

...was stopped by a policeman.........

Yes, officer, what can I do for you?

......He said to him.....

Excuse me, sir...Sorry to trouble you... but you do not appear to be displaying a *TAX DISC*....

.....He said to *him*.....

Oh I'm *FRIGHTFULLY* Sorry, Sergeant!

Constable, actually, Sir

Constable! My new disc arrived in the post this morning...*CLEAN* forgot to put it on! ..The old one.... whole shooting-match dropped orf the windscreen... Then my children were playing with it...*lost* it... and, really, I....I..

Awfully careless, I *AM* Sorry!

...and the consequence was:

Yeah, well... that's all right, Sir.

Make sure you put your new one on, when you get home, mind...

Absolutely! Will do!

Right, mind how you go, then....

Row 2

The owner of an expensive car....

...was addressed by a policeman....

Excuse me....

....He said to her...

You realise you could be causing an obstruction, waiting here, don't you?

Your husband's car, is it?

...She said to him....

No, I'm not married

Borrowed the boyfriend's car, eh?

No, it's my car...

May I see your licence, please?

...and the consequence was:

Yes, well that seems to be in order...all right? Mind how you go, then...

Row 3

The owner of an expensive car.....

uh oh!

...saw that he was about to be stopped by a policeman...

...who was about to say to him......

Fancy car...where did you nick this, then, eh?

It's MY car!

A likely story!

He said to himself.....

I'm *NOT* driving in there! I *HATE* Consequences!

......and drove straight off to another page...

Oi!

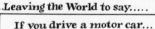

Hey! You can't just drive off! That's not playing the game!

...Leaving the World to say.....

If you drive a motor car... You'll get stopped, the chances are. But as a rule, you'll be all right, If you're male and posh and white.

© Posy Simmonds 1986

© Posy Simmonds 1985

A Kind of Liberation

In the lunch-break, *George Weber* and a colleague nip out...each to do his shopping....

37 BATES

What's the matter, George? Have I upset you?

George?

Have I upset you? I have...haven't I?

NO!

Well.....as a...um matter of fact... ...**YES**...you have...

Um...your behaviour in there...in the green-grocer's...

Oh! You mean I **CAMPED** it up a bit?

Yes!

37

Yes...well, I *did*... I admit I did..... I am **GAY**, after all....

I *know* you are!

Oh, but for Heaven's sake, don't *THINK* for a minute that's *why* I...er...*No,no, NO!* .....It's just..er...that you don't *usually* ...er....

...Behave like a raving queen...?

No...I don't, usually....

...But that bloke in there...he got *right up* my nose!

Him...going *ON* and *ON* about us doing the shopping for our *lucky WIVES*.... got *right* on my wick ....*EVERYWHERE* the assumption that *EVERYONE* is HETEROSEXUAL!!

I **CAN'T STAND** being treated like a *HOUSE-HUSBAND!*

That's all very well...but what about *ME*, now!?

You're all right..you **ARE** a kind of house-husband!

YES! *Years* I've been going in that shop...he's OK, that bloke.....I mean, for a long time, he used to *TEASE* me...about why it was always *ME* that did the shopping & cooking for the family...He thought: *REAL MEN DON'T DO THE SHOPPING*...*REAL MEN DON'T DO HOUSE-WORK*...*REAL MEN DON'T make vichyssoise*...

...But since then, we've had quite a few *CHATS*...you know, about the changing *rôles* of men & women... and he's just come round to the idea that it's *NORMAL* to share domestic work — it's not *unmanly* to do the shopping etc...you know: the whole *TOUGH/TENDER* conflation....

And then **YOU** go in there and do your number...

..and now I'm afraid he may be back where I started.....

I told him... **REAL MEN** don't do the shopping...

© Posy Simmonds 1985

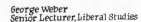

© Posy Simmonds 1984

In a large bookshop, best-selling author, J.D. Crouch is signing copies of the second volume of his trilogy of social historical novels, "The Harlow Years"..... ("...Provocative in its attempt at a panoptic vision..." T.L.S.)

The Harlow Years J D CROUCH

Hallo! — Would you like this signed for anyone in particular? — O! That would be LOVELY! — To Anne, with an E... — Thanks so much!

Funny, I imagined him to be a much SMALLER man! — yes!

MEET J.D. CROUCH IN PERSON 2·30-3·30

..Happy Christmas Ian...and... June.... — And can I say HOW much I enjoy your work... — Oh, how very, very kind of you! — ...Specially all the RAUNCHY bits!!

Well, raunchiness is not exactly what I intend... I just try for a little straightforwardness... — Thank you so much!

Hallo — Would you like this signed for anybody? — Oh! For Penny — I'm SUCH a fan! Got all your books! — SWEET of you!

Hallo — Would you like it signed for anyone? — No, just your signature, please... — Thank you so much!

...S'funny, we imagined you'd be small & wiry, like your Thorold Bates, in "Out of Flatley" — O how amusing!

B·r·o·w·n·e... with an e... — Thank you so much!

...HOW you get your writing to be so fluid and natural? — You ARE kind!! But you know, "Ars est celare artem" ...and all that! — I do a bit of scribbling, myself... and I wondered if I might send you..er... if you had time, that is...

...Just my signature? ...Righto...

Hallo — Ooh, what a lot of books! Thank you so much! — Who would you like them for...? — To Barbra with two A's

...who you gave a black eye to in 1975, you bastard! — Ark! — Barbra!

What're you doing here!!? GO AWAY! I'll see you later! — I want you to sign my books!

These are for all the people I witnessed you plagiarise.... — This one for Kingsley Amis... — You ripped off whole speech patterns from 'Girl, 20'....

One for John Updike, whose metaphors you're so fond of... — And you owe these to Alan Sillitoe and Günter Grass... for nicking their characters' central dilemmas...

And now for FAMILY ones... One for me, Barbra...Two A's... ...your ex-wife, whose maintenance you stopped in 1982..... — Go AWAY! Go AWAY!

One for your children, Rachel & Toby, who you never bother to see, but about whom you talk so fondly in interviews.....

...and one for Teresa, your researcher, now Mrs Crouch — ...who you were knocking off, when I was in hospital having Toby... — Thank you so much! I'll collect them later

Has she gone?

Funny, I imagined him to be a much BIGGER man...

© Posy Simmonds 1986

© Posy Simmonds 1987

Cutting the cord

George Weber is having a vexatious time with his eldest daughter....

The little..!

She **has**! She's gone and propositioned him!

GERK! Who?

Belinda and **Stanhope**, that's who...

Ooh...bit of an *Oh Christ* situation, eh?

I'll say!

Randy old SOD, Stanhope... ...**flash** as a **rat** with a **gold tooth**! HAR Haaaa!

Tsk! Calls himself a **friend**...I'm **not** having **HIM** and **my** daughter....

But, what would your fiancé say?

Oh, **do** say **YES**...

O, darling, you know how I **adore** you!

.....I mean... I remember **you** in your **carry-cot**....

Believe me, I'm **very, very** touched and flattered.... **much as** I'd **love** to...but what would your **Dad** say?

Nothing to do with him, now!

He refused to do it! He **said**: he didn't **own** me....**I** wasn't his **property**...I'm a **free agent**...

Even so, **I** might feel a tiny bit **terrible**...

YOU might feel a **tiny bit terrible!?**...What about **ME?!**

I'm **not** having **HER** and **YOU**...

Shuddup, Dad!

It's none of your business, now!

YOU said you didn't **OWN** me!... **YOU** said I'm **not** your property! **YOU** said you'd rather **die** than hand me over like a **chattel**! **YOU** said you'd feel a **berk** in a **penguin suit**..!

...That's why I've **every** right to ask **Stanhope** to give me away at my **wedding**.....

..and if he won't do it, I'll ask **Edmund**!

YOU'd give me away, **Edmund**, wouldn't you?

Anything you **shay**, **shweetheart**!

You're bloody **NOT**, Edmund!!! ...or **YOU**, Stanhope!...look, she's **MY** daughter, not **YOURS**!

Too late, Dad

Wait!...**look!** I **do** appreciate the need for some sort of **ritual**..er.. behaviour on my part.....an **exogamous paradigm**... um...

I agree to **ACCOMPANY** you up the aisle..**O.K?**...as your **equal**...

Yeah?

But, do you, Dad, promise to **hire** a **suit** and to **cut** the **cr*p**, as **long as** the **service** lasts?

Speak now...or forever **hold** your **codpiece**!

© **Posy Simmonds** 1987

Wedding Party Politics

Photographs taken by Barry Parry.... *(Alliance)*

Can you all squeeze up a bit...? Lovely! MAGIC!

...at the wedding of Miss Belinda Weber, *(Conservative)*

...eldest daughter of Mr and Mrs George Weber,.... *(Staunch Labour)* *(Green Party)*

God, I feel a **berk**! God, I feel a **berk**!

DO shut **up**, George!

...and Mr Alistair Razer-Dorke, *(Conservative)*

...son of Lt Col and Mrs Desmond Razer-Dorke. *(Deep-dyed Conservative)*

Oe garsh! **ISN'T** cheap champagne absolute **HELL**!

GENERAL BREAKDOWN OF WEDDING PARTY:

Lab SDP Lab Green Lab. Con. Con. Con. Con. Con. Con. Con.

Con. Lab. All.

Mr Edmund Heep. *(spoiled ballot paper)*

My votesha shecret between me 'n' the **ballock boxsh**!

Mr Stanhope Wright *(ex fair weather Labour, Soi-disant S.D.P/closet Conservative).* sharing a joke with Mr Edmund Heep.

How many people does it take to circumcise a whale?......

Dunno

Four Skin-divers

Mrs Stanhope Wright *(Tactical Voter)* **and Miss Jocasta Wright** *(Don't Know, Don't Care)*

Mr Julian Heep *(Red Caucus)* **Mr Jolyon Heep** *(Conservative)*

You little **Tory git**, Jolly!

You **anarchist berk**, Jules!

Mr Kevin Penwallet *(Mebyon Kernow)*

Come again?

Mrs Brinsley Bowe *(Con)* **& her daughter, Penny** *(Lab)*

Benji and Sophie Weber *(Alliance)*

Mr Edmund Heep reading the telemessages.

It says: Please send **photo** of couple..... ...**not MOUNTED**...just holding hands!

Harhaar Haa!

Booze has given out...

...O God..this wedding... ...it's **the end**!.....

Goodbye!

Goodbye!

Bye Bye

Bye Bye

© Posy Simmonds 1987

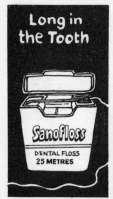

© Posy Simmonds 1986

Thinking of you this Christmastide......

It's not even midnight when Stanhope returns from the office Christmas bash.....

Blimey O'Reilly! You're EARLY!

Well... you know.... same old, boring faces... same old crappitty-crap...

Actually, I think I'm getting **flu**....

Not AGAIN!

That's what comes of *burning* your whatsit at both ends....

But what are the symptoms?

Anyway, one just **can't** be *too* careful....

Stanhope...I've left all your relations' ones for **you** to do

Wot?

Christmas cards.... ...for all your aunts and cousins......

Oh, sod THAT!

Tsk! God, REALLY! One year to the next, you don't give a *monkey's* about your relations, do you?

My *relations* ??..... ..on the contrary, I'm **OBSESSED** with them!

My relations with *Helen*, after the **D & AD** awards...

Well.. nothing to worry about there... ...... is there?

...And *Vicki* ?

No..... sure we're O.K.

..But **PENNY!** ¡GULP!

God, she knows some really *weird* men!

Because, I mean! you just can't **TELL**, can you? You can have it... ...have **AIDS** for months without **knowing**....

..Now on, just have to really look where I leap....

Stanhope...what're you doing in there...?

Drinking to my *relations*...... their *good health*...

© Posy Simmonds 1986

Good Sports

In the games at Katie's birthday party, there are NO *winners* and NO *losers*......

♪ Get into the groove girl...you gotta give your love to m

I'm the **WINNER AGAIN!**

Right, now...

Tamsin's the last one in...so she gets to give everyone a prize...

I'm the winner!

Hey, I got a **Snowman** pad and pencil!

But **I** was the winner...

You see, the *important* thing in *games* is NOT to *win*...but to *take* part....

Oh, I so **agree!**

Well, I think it's a good idea... **NO** declared winners....

I mean, it's what they do at **Rachel's** school, now...you know, *non-competitive* games & sports...

Right...now *is* everybody a *sleeping lion*?

You're not, Benji!

...the children just play co-operatively... ...just enjoy the game for itself....

And **you**, Fanny! Out you go!

Much fairer at parties...cos' you **always** get **one** or **two** kids, who **NEVER** win **anything!**

Oh, **MORTIFYING** for them! ....Terrible *boo-hoos*, all the way home!

Doesn't *matter*, darling! Not **everyone** can win! *Not* the end of the world...you got a going home present...

BOO HOO!

And I won a My Little Pony money box!

Oh God, I mean, **I** remember children's parties! ....**Just HELL ON EARTH!** I was **always** out **first** go... I **never** won!

Out goes **Lucy!** ..And it's Tamsin left! The **only** sleepy Leo the Lion...

Well! Well!

...The **HUMILIATION** of always *losing!* It's **so damaging** for the kids' *self-image*....they learn to **think** of themselves as **losers**....

So Tamsin gets to give out the *going-home* presents....**o.k?**

This way, everyone gets a present....

And everyone's happy!

Ah yes!

Look!

Mum! Look what I got!

Oh, Tamsin! Come on, cheer up! You've got **exactly** the same amount of presents as they have! **Everyone** got the same...

Bud dey didernt WIN dem! BOO HOO! I was the WINNER!

BOO HOOOO!

© Posy Simmonds 1987